Horizons

The Deer in the Woods

Horizons Phonics and Reading 1
Reader 2

Author:	Polly A. Wood, M.A.
Editor:	Alan L. Christopherson, M.S.
Illustrations:	Keith Piccolo, Karen Eubanks, Greg Capps, Steve Ring, Kirk Headley, Kyle Bennett, Brian McCracken
Layout Design:	Lauren Durain, A.S.T.

Alpha Omega Publications, Inc. • Rock Rapids, IA

Printed in the United States of America

ISBN 978-0-7403-0322-7

A Note to Teachers and Parents

The Horizons First Grade Phonics Readers are to be used as a companion to the Horizons First Grade Student Workbooks. For each lesson in the Student Workbooks there is a corresponding story in the Readers. The story will illustrate and demonstrate the primary concept of the lesson. Most first grade students should not be expected to read the first forty stories independently. The teacher or parent should read the stories to the student. The student can sound out some of the shorter, single syllable words. After lesson forty, most first grade students should be able to start reading the stories independently. The student may still require some help with some of the words. The teacher or parent should make word cards for the words that the student does not know. The word cards should be reviewed with the student frequently. As the student's vocabulary increases, the student may be able to go back to the first forty stories and read them independently.

The teacher or parent should ask the student questions before and after reading the story. Help the student anticipate what is going to happen in the story after reading the title or looking at the pictures. There are comprehension questions at the end of each story. The answers to these questions should be discussed. If so desired, the teacher or parent may have the student write out the answers to the questions.

At this stage, the skill level of each student will vary. It is not necessary for the student to sound out and read every word in a story. This skill will develop gradually over the course of this unit. Enjoy the learning process as it happens!

Table of Contents

Lesson #	Title	Page

Lesson #	Title	Page

The Letter to Grandma

Meg wrote a letter to her grandma. Meg told her grandma all about what she had been doing in school and about her soccer team. She also told Grandma about her friends, and what things she had been doing with them.

Meg started the letter on Monday. She wrote some more on Tuesday. She had to redo that part, because she had not used her best spelling. On Wednesday, she wrote some more. On Thursday, she wanted to write some more, but she didn't have time. She finished

the letter on Friday. She took the letter to her older sister, Jen, to check the spelling.

Jen said, "Meg, you'll need to rewrite this. Your handwriting isn't very good. You need to fix some of the spelling. I'll circle the words that you need to fix. Then you'll have to rewrite it and do a neater job."

Jen circled the words that Meg needed to fix and gave the letter back to her.

"Here you go," Jen said. 'If you need any more help, let me know."

"Thanks, Jen," said Meg.

Meg took the letter back to her room to work on. She rewrote all of the words that

she needed to fix. Then she got a new piece of paper and began rewriting the letter. She used her best handwriting and her best

spelling. She put the letter in the mailbox.

A week later, she got a letter back from Grandma. Grandma said that she loved Meg's letter and that she was pleased with Meg's nice handwriting and spelling. Meg was glad that she had rewritten the letter. She was sure that she would do a great job next time.

1. How many days did it take Meg to write the letter to Grandma?
2. How did Jen help Meg with her letter?
3. What did Meg have to do to the letter before she sent it?

Grocery Shopping

Jason and his dad went grocery shopping. They went every week on Saturday. Jason got to help Dad pick out what they needed. He helped put things into the cart. Dad liked to have Jason's help. Dad always told Jason that if he was good and didn't ask for things, he could get a treat on the way out of the store.

They always needed milk, bread, and eggs. They got fruit, vegetables, soup, and cereal. Sometimes, Dad would get something special, like cookies or ice cream. Jason liked to pick out the flavors.

When they were finished shopping and had paid for the groceries, Jason always helped dad to put the

groceries into the car. After they got home, Jason would help Dad unload the groceries and unpack the bags in the house. He also helped put things away. Sometimes, Dad's arms were full of bags and Jason would unlock the door to the house.

Jason was glad that helping Dad do the grocery shopping was his job. He would be unhappy if he didn't get to do it.

1. What did Jason do to help at the grocery store?
2. What did Jason do to help when he and Dad got home?
3. What would Jason get if he were good at the store?

Charlie's Chores

Charlie had chores that he had to do every day. He had to make his bed, wind his alarm clock, and pack his backpack for school. He also read at least one book every night before he went to bed.

One day, he had a hard time doing his jobs. He got up late, so he was in a hurry to get to school. He made his bed, but he didn't do it well. He didn't wind his alarm clock, and he didn't pack his backpack.

When his mom called to him, he was just about to walk out the door to go to school.

"Charlie, come in here please!" his mom called. "You need to do your chores!"

Charlie said, "I'm going to be late. Can I do them later?"

Mom said, "Okay, but you will have to do them right away when you get home."

When Charlie got to school, he didn't have what he needed. He had left his books and his homework at home. He hadn't repacked his backpack before he left that day.

When he got home, he had to remake his bed. He did a better job this time. He also had to rewind his alarm clock. It had run down and was not telling the correct time anymore.

After he was done, Charlie told his mom. She was glad that he had done the things that he needed to.

"Now, you'll have the things that you need for school, be able to tell the right time, and have a neatly made bed," said Mom. "Aren't you glad?"

Charlie said, "Yes, I am. I won't have to redo things."

1. What were Charlie's chores?
2. Why did Charlie have to redo his chores?
3. Do you think he will have to redo his jobs again?

The Disorderly Room

Jake's room was a mess. His mom said that it was disorderly. She said that his room was a disgrace. She said that she disliked the mess. She told Jake to clean it up right away. She would not let him play until he cleaned up his disorderly room.

Jake looked at the disorder. He didn't know where to start. His toys were everywhere. His bed was a mess. There were clothes all over the floor. He thought he would start with his toys. He got out his toy box. It was already full. How did that happen? Did he really play with those toys? He started cleaning out the toy box. Then he would have more room.

As he started to clean out the toy box, he saw that he was making more of a mess. The room was even more disorderly than it was before.

Still, he kept on. He put all of the toys that he didn't want into a pile. Mom could take them to the church. The pastor could give them away to children who needed them. Jake then put all of the toys that he did want into the toy box. Everything fit just fine.

He then started on the clothes that were on the floor. He took the ones that were dirty and put them into his hamper. He put the clean ones away.

His bed was last. He pulled up the sheet and the blanket and then the spread. He smoothed it all out. Then, he fluffed up his pillow and put it at the head of the bed.

Jake stood back to look at his room. It had been hard work, but it was no longer  disorderly or a disgrace. His mom would be proud. He went to tell her that he was finished.

"Wow!" said Mom. "This looks good!"

"I disagree," said Jake.

"What?" said Mom.

"It looks great!" cried Jake.

1. Why was Jake's mom upset about his room?
2. How did Jake get all of his toys to fit into the toy box?
3. Do you think that Jake will let his room become disorderly again? Why or why not?

The Disagreeing Girls

Mandy and Shelly couldn't agree on anything. They lived next door to each other, and they were in the same class at school, so they were together just about every day. They just saw things differently.

They disagreed about what animals they liked. Mandy liked dogs, and Shelly liked cats. Mandy liked lizards and Shelly liked rabbits.

They disagreed about what they liked at school. Shelly liked reading the best, and Mandy liked math the best. Shelly liked reading because she was a good reader. She disliked

math because it was hard for her. Mandy liked math because it was easy for her. Reading was hard for Mandy.

One day, Mandy and Shelly were disagreeing about the story that the class was reading. Shelly said that the story was about a boy who disobeyed his mom and dad. Mandy said that the story was about a boy who went to the park. Mrs. Rath, their teacher, came over to see what was going on.

"Girls, what is wrong?" Mrs. Rath asked.

"We can't agree about the story," said Mandy. "I say that the story is about a boy who

disobeys. Shelly says it is about a boy who goes to the park to play."

Mrs. Rath said, "Why don't you reread the story together, and then you will both know."

"All right. Let's go reread the story," said Shelly.

Mandy and Shelly got their reading books out of their desks. They took turns reading the story. Shelly helped Mandy read the words that she wasn't sure about.

After they had finished reading, Mandy said, "Thanks for helping me read. I couldn't read some of the words, so I didn't really know what the story was

about. I guess we were both right. The boy disobeyed his mom and dad and went to the park to play instead of doing his chores."

Shelly said, "I was happy to help you read the story. Maybe we should help each other more often, and not disagree all the time."

"Yes, that is a good idea. Maybe next time I can help you with math," said Mandy.

1. What did Mandy like the best in school?
2. What did Shelly like the best in school?
3. How did the girls solve their disagreement about the story?

The Bride on the Train

Joey was riding the train with his dad. They were riding home from a trip to the city. They had been to a baseball game. They were happy, but tired.

Joey saw something that he had not seen before. At the next stop, a lady got on the train. She was all dressed in white. She had a veil on her head that was made of white lace. She had a long, full white dress on. She was a bride! She looked

very pretty. Joey had never seen a bride in person before, so this was something new to him.

All of the other people on the train were looking at the bride. They were talking softly to one another about her. Joey could tell that the bride knew the people were talking about her, because her face turned red.

Another lady who was sitting next to the bride started talking to her. Joey could hear them. The lady was asking the bride where she was getting married and at what time. The bride answered that she was getting married at the church downtown at 7:00 that night. Joey looked at his watch. That was in three hours.

After awhile, the train came to the next stop. The bride got her purse and made her way carefully off the train. She did not want to get her dress dirty.

Some of the people waved good-bye to the bride and said "good luck."

The next stop was Joey's. He and his dad got off the train. They walked to their car. As they were driving home, Joey thought about how much fun it had been to see the pretty bride. Joey hoped that everything went well for her.

1. Where had Joey and his dad been?
2. How did Joey know that the lady who got on the train was a bride?
3. Why did the bride's face turn red?

Sledding

It is fun to go sledding. There should be a lot of snow on the ground to go sledding. You do not want to hit the dirt. You want to stay on your sled. You can also play in the snow when you go sledding.

There are many different kinds of sleds. There is the wooden kind with the metal slides on the bottom. Most of them have a rope that you can use to steer the sled.

Another kind of sled is the saucer. It is a silver circle with two handles. One or two people can sit in it. It goes very fast!

When you go sledding, you need to know some safety rules. You should never sled near trees or other large plants. You might sled into one of them and hurt yourself.

You should make sure that there is enough snow on the ground so that you don't hit the dirt with your sled. You could stop suddenly and fly off your sled.

Do not have too many people on your sled. You could fall on top of one another and everyone could get hurt.

Sledding can be a lot of fun if you go when there is enough snow on the ground and you follow the safety rules.

1. Why does there have to be a lot of snow on the ground for it to be safe to go sledding?
2. What are the rules for sledding safely?
3. Can you think of some more rules for sledding safety?

The Parade

The high school band was marching in a parade. Because it was November, it was cold outside. All of the band members had gloves on to keep their hands warm. Their clothes were warm, so they didn't wear coats.

The band marched down Main Street. All of the people in the crowd cheered for them. The band stopped and played a song for the people. After they finished the song, they marched on.

The band stopped by a bridge and played another song for the people who were there watching the parade. When they were finished, they marched on.

There were clowns in the parade also. They came right after the band. They played games with one another and threw candy to the crowd of people.

There were trucks carrying the mayor of the town and other important people. The trucks drove slowly. The people waved.

When the parade was over, the people went home. The band members were tired from all of that marching.

They were glad to go home and sit down!

1. Why was it cold outside?
2. Where did the band stop to play songs?
3. What did the clowns do in the parade?

Tammy's Vacation

Tammy's teacher, Mrs. Reed, was having her students write about a fun family vacation that they'd had. Tammy wrote about her family's camping trip to the woods.

Tammy wrote about how long it had taken to drive there. They were tired by the time they got to their

camping spot. They set up their tent and unloaded their food and clothes into the tent. Then, they wanted to go hiking.

They hiked up to the top of a hill. From the hill, they could see all around. It was very pretty. Then, they hiked back down and went back to camp and had hot dogs and beans for supper. They made a campfire and cooked some marshmallows. Then, it was time for sleep.

The next day, they went fishing at a lake. They caught quite a few fish and took the fish back to camp to have for supper that night. The fish were very good!

The next day, it was time to go home. They packed the tent and all of their gear into the car. They were sad to be going home, but they were ready to sleep in their own beds.

Tammy's teacher liked her story. Tammy got to read it to the class. At the end, Tammy added that she hoped she and her family would get to go camping again.

1. What were the students writing about?
2. What did Tammy and her family do on their vacation?
3. How did Tammy and her family feel about going home?

The Snake Slithered

Stan had a snake. It was a small, green snake. It was a garter snake. He kept his snake in a glass cage. There were grass and sticks in the cage so that the snake would feel as if he was outside. Stan fed insects to the snake. That was

what the snake would have eaten if he were living outside.

Stan sometimes took his snake out of his cage. Stan would take him outside to slither in the grass. Stan had to keep an eye on the snake because the snake was green like the grass and could get lost.

Stan's mom didn't like the snake and wouldn't let Stan have him loose in the house. One time, the snake got out of his cage when Stan had forgotten to put the lid on. Mom screamed when she saw the snake. After that, Stan kept the lid on the cage.

Stan took the snake to school for show and tell. He took his snake out of the cage so that the kids could pet it. Everyone thought that the snake would be slimy, but they were surprised that it wasn't.

Stan showed the kids how to pet the snake, starting from the head and going to the tail. The teacher said that the snake was fun and she thanked Stan for bringing it.

Stan thought that a snake was the best pet anyone could have. It didn't make noise, and he didn't have to sweep up after it.

1. What kind of a snake did Stan have?
2. What happened when the snake got out of the cage?
3. Was the snake slimy?
4. What is the best way to pet a snake?

The Happy Baby

Tommy is a happy baby. He smiles a lot. He laughs a lot, too. He likes everybody.

There aren't too many things that make baby Tommy cry. He will cry if he is hungry, tired, or wet. Other than that, he is happy. He is fun to play with.

His brother, Sam, likes to play with Tommy. They play peek-a-boo and roll a little ball to each other. Tommy is learning how to throw the ball. He laughs when he does it right. Sam also likes to try to fly Tommy through the air by holding him like an airplane.

When Tommy is sleepy, he will be fussy. Then, Mom or Dad rocks Tommy and takes him to his crib. Sometimes, he needs a dry diaper.

Tommy has a stuffed bunny that he likes to play with. He hugs his bunny and talks baby talk.

Everybody likes Tommy because he is so much fun. Sam's friends wish that they had a baby brother just like Tommy.

1. What might make Tommy cry?
2. What games does Tommy like to play with Sam?
3. What does Tommy do with his stuffed bunny?

John's Thirteenth Birthday

John's mom asked him what he would like to do for his thirteenth birthday. John said that he didn't know. He thought about it for a few days, but he couldn't come up with anything that he and his family hadn't already done.

John's mom said, "How about going to the park?"

"No," said John, "That's no good."

"How about the movies?" John's mom asked.

"No, I want to do something special.

That's something that we always do," said John.

"We could go to the amusement park," said Mom.

"No, not that!" said John.

"Well, I am out of ideas. Let me know if you think of something," said Mom.

John thought and thought. He asked his friends the next day at school.

"You could go swimming," said Theo.

"No, the pool gets too crowded," said John.

"How about going out to eat?" said Ron.

"We do that a lot," said John.

"Boy, are you hard to please!" said Theo.

That day after school, John was watching TV. He saw an ad for a new ice skating rink. John had never been ice skating, but he was willing to learn. He thought that it sounded like fun. He told his mom.

"Mom, I think that I've finally thought of something to do for my birthday," said John. "I'd like to go ice skating at the new rink in town."

"I haven't been ice skating in years," said Mom, "but, I'd like to go, too. I'm sure that your dad would agree."

John and his mom and dad went ice skating for John's thirteenth birthday. John thought that it was the best time he ever had!

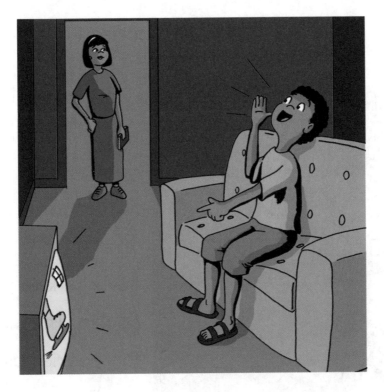

1. Why didn't John want to go to the movies for his birthday?
2. How did John find out about the ice skating rink?
3. Did John and his family have fun ice skating?

A Batch of Cookies

Martha and her sister made a batch of cookies. They made butterscotch cookies. That was their dad's favorite kind of cookie. They made the cookies as a surprise for him.

Martha made their batch of cookies in the kitchen. They knew how to make the cookies from watching their mother do it. Their mom watched while they worked.

They took turns stirring the dough. First, Martha stirred, then Jenny stirred, and then they switched back. They had fun doing it that way, and their arms didn't get tired.

When the cookies were done, they put them into a bag and sealed it so that the cookies would stay fresh. They put the bag in the kitchen pantry.

After dinner, Martha and Jenny told their dad that they had a surprise for him. They went to the kitchen pantry and got the bag of cookies. They gave the cookies to Dad. He was very surprised!

Dad said, "Thanks girls! These look very good. Let's have some now."

"Sure," said Martha. "We've been waiting all day to eat these."

They each had three cookies. They all enjoyed them, especially Dad.

Dad said, "You'll have to be sure and make these again, girls. Good job!"

1. What kind of cookies did Martha and Jenny make?
2. Why did they make that kind of cookie?
3. When did Dad and the girls eat the cookies?

The Pitcher in the Kitchen

Mona's mother had a beautiful pitcher. It was made of glass. Mother used it for iced tea or lemonade. It was for special times when they had guests. Mona loved the pitcher.

One day, Mona went into the kitchen looking for something to do. She went to the pantry and found some lemonade mix. She looked for something to make

it in. All of the plastic pitchers were being used. She thought about Mother's glass pitcher.

Mother had gone to the store, so she wasn't there for Mona to ask. "I think she'd say that it was okay. I'll be careful," thought Mona. So she took the pitcher out of the cabinet where it was kept.

Mona carefully set the pitcher on the counter. She poured the lemonade mix into the pitcher. As she was taking it to the sink to fill it with water, the pitcher slipped out of her hands and broke all over the floor.

Mona stood there, not knowing what to do next. She knew that she was going to be in trouble because she had used the pitcher without asking. She also knew that she had to clean up the mess it had made. Mona got the broom and dustpan and swept up the broken glass. She dumped the mess into the trash. Just then, Mother walked into the kitchen.

"What was that sound? It sounded like something broken being thrown into the trash," Mother said.

Mona knew that she couldn't lie to her mother. She was too scared to say anything.

"Well, what was it?" Mother asked again.

"I'm sorry, Mother," Mona said softly. "I was using your pitcher to make lemonade and I broke it. I didn't mean to!"

"Mona, that was my special pitcher. You should have

waited until I got home to ask me if you could use it," Mother said.

"I know, and I'm so sorry," said Mona sadly.

"Well, you'll have to pay for it out of your allowance. I'll take one dollar out each week until it is paid for," said Mother.

"I understand," said Mona, as she walked slowly out of the kitchen and into her room.

Mona learned a good lesson that day. She would think first before she did something and would always ask before she used any of Mother's special things.

1. Why did Mona use Mother's pitcher for lemonade?
2. What happened to the pitcher?
3. Do you think that Mona's punishment was fair?

Shiny Shells

When Shannon goes to the beach, she looks for shells. The shells come in many different sizes and colors. Some of the shells are broken and some are all in one piece.

The ones that Shannon likes the best are the shiny shells. There are tiny shells and there are bigger shells that Shannon thinks she can hear the ocean in. Most of the shiny shells have some pink color in different places. The shiny spots are very smooth. Shannon likes feeling the smooth parts with her fingers.

Shannon keeps the shiny shells as part of a collection in her room. She puts the shells in a box lined with cotton balls so that the shells won't get broken. Every time Shannon goes to the beach, she finds some shells for her collection.

Shannon likes to take the shell collection to school to show her teacher, Mrs. Shaw. Mrs. Shaw says that most of the shells were once homes for crabs and other ocean animals. The animals used the shells for protection against other animals that wanted to eat them. Mrs. Shaw always likes to see the new shells that Shannon shows her.

Shannon has gotten some of her friends to collect other things. They see her shell collection and start collecting things that they like. It is fun to collect things. Shannon is glad that her friends enjoy her shell collection.

1. Where does Shannon look for shells?

2. What were most shells used for?

3. How do the shiny parts feel?

A Chip Sandwich

Chad was hungry when he got home from school. He didn't know what he wanted to eat. He looked in the pantry, but nothing looked good. He checked the refrigerator, but there  was nothing in there that he wanted either. He decided to watch TV.

Chad was watching cartoons when he saw an ad for potato chips. They really looked good! Chad checked the pantry again. He thought he had seen a bag of chips before. Sure enough, there was a bag of chips in the back of the pantry.

Chad took the bag of chips to the kitchen table and got a handful of chips out of the bag. He started munching on them. He got tired of just chips after awhile. What else could he have? He checked the pantry again. He saw the bread and the peanut butter. Then he had an idea! What about a chip sandwich? He could put peanut butter on the bread and add the chips in the middle. It sounded good, so he decided to try it.

Chad took the bread and peanut butter to the table. He made his chip sandwich. He took a bite. He thought it tasted great! It was crunchy, but creamy

at the same time. Chad got himself a glass of milk to wash it down with. He was proud of his new kind of sandwich.

He was so proud that he told his mom when she got home. Mom said, "That sounds good, but no more. We're going to eat dinner soon."

Chad felt like asking her if he could have another chip sandwich for dinner!

1. How did Chad make his chip sandwich?
2. Why did Chad make the chip sandwich?
3. How did Chad's mom feel about the chip sandwich?

The Cherry Tree

Sheryl and Shawn have a cherry tree in the backyard. It is a big tree. It has been there for a long time.

Every spring, the tree grows pretty pink flowers, called blossoms. The blossoms will become cherries in the summer. Sheryl likes the springtime the best because the tree has the blossoms then. Shawn likes the summer best because he likes to eat the cherries.

Sheryl and Shawn also like to play around the cherry tree. They like to climb on its branches. They make sure to stay on the lower branches to be safe. Sheryl and Shawn also like the shade that the tree gives in summer when it is hot.

When Sheryl and Shawn pick the cherries in the summer, their mom makes all kinds of good things with them. She freezes some, makes jelly with some, and makes pies and  tarts with the rest. The whole family loves the cherry treats.

Sheryl and Shawn like the cherry tree so much that they each plan on planting cherry trees in their own yards when they grow up.

1. What do the cherries start out to be on the tree?
2. What do Sheryl and Shawn do around the cherry tree?
3. What does Mom do with the cherries?

Zach's Report

Zach's teacher told the students that they were going to be doing reports about animals. She told them that they were to think of three animals that they might like to report on, and then choose the one that they liked the best. That would be the animal that they would write their report about.

The teacher passed out animal books to the students. She told them that they could use those books for ideas for the report. Zach took a book about snakes. He liked snakes. He had seen snakes at the pet store near his

house. He had also seen snakes on a show on TV. He knew a little bit about snakes, so he thought he would do his report about snakes.

First, he read some of the snake books. Then, he picked three of the books that told the most about snakes. Then, Zach wrote some notes about snakes. He wrote about what snakes ate, where they lived, how they had their babies, how snakes moved, and many other things. Then, he wrote an outline for his report. Zach wrote the facts that he wanted to put into the report. He wrote the facts in order on a piece of paper.

After Zach wrote the outline for his report, he used it to write the report. He wrote a rough draft, which is just the first copy of the report. Then, he had his writing partner, Billy, read the report. Billy helped Zach with spelling mistakes. Billy also helped Zach rewrite some of the report so that it would make more sense.

After Zach had fixed the mistakes in the report, he wrote the final copy of the report on a clean piece of paper and gave it to his teacher. She said that he had done very well!

1. How did Zach think of something to write about?
2. What did Zach do before he wrote the report?
3. How did Billy help Zach with his report?

The Sandbox in the Backyard

Max and his little sister, Jen, liked to play in the sandbox in their backyard. Jen was only two years old, so the sand was always fun for her. Jen and Max did many things in the sandbox.

Max liked to make sand castles. He used the buckets and plastic shovels to make the castles. He got water and wet the sand so that it would stay together better. He also liked to pretend that he was making pies and cupcakes out of the sand. He had some sand toys that let the sand go through different places and all come out one end. He really liked to play with those toys.

Jen liked to do other things with the sand. She liked to use the shovel to put the sand into the buckets. She would pat the sand with her hands until it was smooth. Jen also liked to get the sand wet and stamp her feet in it. She liked the cold feeling of the sand. One thing she liked that she wasn't allowed to do was throw the sand. She thought that it was fun, but got into trouble when she did it.

When Jen and Max were done playing with the sand, they would clean up the sand toys with water, dry them off, and put them into a backpack until they played with them again.

1. What did Max like to do in the sandbox?
2. What did Jen like to do in the sandbox?
3. What did Jen like to do that she wasn't allowed to do?

Kip, A Playful Puppy

Mary's dog, Kip, was a very playful puppy. He was still a baby, so he was small. He ran all around. He liked to have fun.

He got into a lot of trouble because he was so playful. He did things that he shouldn't do. Once, he got into the bathroom and unrolled all of the paper. Another time, he jumped onto the sofa and tried to lie on the back of it. He fell off the back of the sofa and almost hurt himself.

Kip sometimes kept the family up at night because he liked to howl. He would howl in the house, so someone would put Kip outside. Then, he would howl outside and he would wake up the neighbors. Everything Mary and her family tried to do about it was useless.

Once, Kip was ill. It was unlike Kip to lie around quietly, so everyone knew that something was wrong with him. Mary and her dad took Kip to the vet. The vet said that Kip needed to be fed some special foods until he was better. After a week, Kip was back to his old self again.

Even though Kip was sometimes too playful, Mary and her family loved Kip. They thought that Kip was the best dog ever.

1. What trouble did Kip get into?

2. How did Kip sometimes keep Mary and her family up at night?

3. What did Mary have to do to get Kip well when he was ill?

The Smiths Repaint the House

Mr. And Mrs. Smith lived on Beal Street with their three children, Sam, Bess, and Ted. They lived in a brown house with white shutters.

Mr. and Mrs. Smith wanted to repaint their house. They disliked the brown color. The paint was peeling off the sides of the house. The paint on the shutters was cracking and peeling also. It looked bad.

The Smiths wanted to paint their house white with blue shutters. There were other white houses on Beal Street, and the Smiths thought that those houses looked nice. It was a clean look.

Mr. and Mrs. Smith, Sam, Bess, and Ted got on their old clothes one Saturday morning. They got set to repaint the house. They got out the cans of paint, the brushes, scrapers, rollers, and ladders. They also put down some big cloths on the ground so that they wouldn't get paint on the grass or on the cement.

The first thing to do was to scrape off the cracked and chipped paint. The new paint wouldn't stick if they didn't do that. It was a hard, long, and boring job, but

it had to be done. Once the scraping was done, The Smiths could start painting.

Mr. and Mrs. Smith were the only ones to climb on the ladders. It would be unsafe for the children to do it. Mrs. Smith disliked being high up on the ladder, so Mr. Smith did the work that had to be done high up on the house.

After they finished repainting the house, the Smiths were proud of their work. The house looked great. The neighbors told the Smiths how nice their house looked. The Smiths' hard work had paid off.

1. Why did the Smiths want to repaint their house?
2. What was the first thing that the Smiths needed to do before they painted the house?
3. Why were Mr. and Mrs. Smith the only ones to climb on the ladders?

Recess Time

It is recess time at school. The boys and girls run out to the playground to play. There are many things for the kids to do at recess.

Tommy and Jimmy play on the climbing bars. They like to go back and forth on the bars. Sometimes, they race each other.

Taylor and Jenna like playing on the swings. They are careful not to swing too high and not to jump off the swings.

Mark likes to play games at recess. He likes to play kickball or tag with his friends. They are not careless when they play. They look out for one another. Mark likes to run. It makes him feel like he is flying.

When the bell rings to come in after recess, the children run quickly to get in line. Their teacher is waiting for them. Another fun recess time will come tomorrow!

1. What do Tommy and Jimmy like to do at recess?
2. How are Taylor and Jenna careful on the swings?
3. What do the children do when the bell rings to come in?

Rainbow Birthday

Char's birthday was going to be at the park. Char's family had set up picnic tables for lunch and decorated with balloons and streamers. It was going to be a fun day.

The party had just gotten started when the sky began to turn dark. The wind began to blow. There was going to be a storm.

Everyone got under the covered area where the picnic tables were. It began to rain. No one knew what to do. People were talking about going home. Char began to cry.

"Today is a bad day," Char cried. "My birthday is over."

"No, we will stay and see what happens," Char's friend Eva said. She could see that Char was upset.

Char's mom served the food. Everyone tried to stay dry under the cover. It was hard, but they did it. They didn't want Char to feel badly.

Char said, "Maybe it wasn't such a good idea to have my party outside."

Mom said, "It was nice outside before. We didn't know that it would get rainy."

By the time everyone had finished eating lunch, the rain had slowed down to a sprinkle. The sun started to come out a little bit.

"Look!" cried Char. "Look over there! It's a rainbow!"

"Wow!" Eva shouted. "It's so pretty! Look how bright it is!"

Everyone at the park stopped to look at the rainbow. It lasted for a long time. Then, the rain stopped. All of the kids at the party ran out to play.

"My birthday turned out well after all," said Char.

"Yes. I have never been to a rainbow birthday before!" said Eva.

1. Where was Char's birthday?
2. What did everyone do when it started to rain?
3. Why did Char's birthday turn out well, even though it rained?

The Medicine

Nancy had a cold. She felt badly. Her nose was stuffy, her head hurt, her throat hurt, and she had a cough. She couldn't go to school because she felt so badly and because she could have given her cold to the other kids in her class.

It was hard for Nancy to get any sleep at night because she felt so awful. The first night that she had the cold, she only slept a little while. She kept her family up with her coughing. Her mom felt sorry for her and wanted Nancy to feel better.

Mom said, "The only way that you are going to feel any better is by taking some medicine. It won't make you well, but it will make you feel better."

"No! I really dislike the taste of medicine, especially cough medicine!" cried Nancy.

"I don't want to be unkind, but I'm afraid that you are going to have to take it whether you like it or not," said Mom.

Mom got the cough medicine and poured a spoonful of it for Nancy. Nancy made a face. She opened her mouth and mom put the spoonful in.

"Yuck!" cried Nancy, after taking the cough medicine. "That's awful!"

"That should help with your stuffy nose too," Mom said.

Nancy looked at the bottle of cough medicine. It had a picture on it of someone who looked as if she liked the medicine. Nancy couldn't understand that at all.

After a while, Nancy began to feel a little bit better. Her mom was right. Medicine did help, even if Nancy disliked the taste. Maybe the person on the bottle of cough medicine looked that way because the medicine had made her feel better, too.

1. How did Nancy keep her family up at night?
2. What did Mom give Nancy the medicine for?
3. What did Nancy think of the picture on the medicine bottle?

The Thank You Note

Bob got a baseball mitt for his birthday. He got it from his grandfather. The mitt was Bob's favorite present. He had wanted a mitt for a long time.

Bob's dad told him that when you get a present from someone, you should write that person a thank you note. Bob thought that was a good idea. Bob and his dad sat down together to write a thank you note to Bob's grandfather. His dad showed him how to set it up.

Bob wrote the date on the right-hand side at the top of the paper. Then, he wrote "Dear Grandpa," below that on the left-hand side. Then,

Bob wrote that he really liked the baseball mitt and that he had wanted one more than anything. He told his grandfather that he planned to use the mitt when he played on his little league baseball team. He would also use it at practices. Bob said thanks once again, and told his grandfather that he hoped to see him soon.

Bob wrote "Yours truly," for the closing and then signed his name under that. Bob's dad helped him spell the words that he didn't know how to spell. Bob's dad also helped him with the punctuation.

Bob read the note to his dad. Dad said that it was a good note. Bob put it in an envelope and mailed it. Bob felt good that he had told his grandfather "thank you" for his nice gift.

1. What did Bob get from his grandfather?
2. Why did Bob write the note?
3. What did Bob's dad help him with?

The Deer in the Woods

Jan saw a deer as she was walking in the woods. The deer was a female, called a doe.

Jan was very quiet. She knew that she had to be silent, or the doe would hear her and run away. Jan found a place behind a bush to watch the doe.

The forest was very still. Jan tried not to move as she sat there behind the bush. The doe was eating leaves.

Jan could see that the doe had a fawn, or baby deer, with her. The fawn was light brown and had a lot of white spots. The fawn came over by its mother to eat leaves.

Jan watched the deer for a long time. They never heard her. Finally, the doe and her fawn walked away to find more food. Jan waited for a minute before she got up. She didn't want to scare the deer if they were still close by.

Jan was happy that she had gotten to see a deer. It was even more special because the doe had a fawn with her. Jan loved the forest, and hoped to go back again, soon.

1. What kind of deer did Jan see?
2. Why did Jan need to stay still and quiet?
3. What was special about seeing this deer?

The Opposite Twins

Tara and Tina were twins. They were both seven years old. They both had brown hair. Since they were twins, they both looked the same. That was about all that was the same about Tara and Tina.

Everyone called them the "opposite twins" because there were so many things about them that were different. Tara liked to wear dresses and play with dolls. Tina liked to wear pants and climb trees and play ball outside. Tara liked quiet, calm games. Tina liked noisy, rough games that had to be played outside. Tara liked to play by herself. Tina

wanted to play with many kids at once. Tina liked things that were old and had gotten a lot of love. Tara wanted everything to be new and unused.

For Tina and Tara's birthday, it was hard for their parents to decide what to do. The girls wanted to have a party, but each girl wanted  something different. Tara wanted to have three of her best friends and have a craft—making party. Tina wanted to have many friends and have the party at a park where they could run and play outside.

Finally, Tina and Tara's parents decided to have two parties. Tara's would be at home the way that she wanted it. Tina's would be at a park and would have games and lots of friends. The parties would be on two different days.

Both of the parties were fun. Their parents worked hard to make each day special. Tina and Tara were thankful to their parents for making their parties so nice, but they decided that they would have one birthday party the following year. It would be easier for everyone!

1. Why were Tina and Tara called the "opposite twins?"
2. Why did Tina and Tara have different birthday parties?
3. What did Tina and Tara decide that they would do for their birthday the following year?

I Sent a Cent

When Jeremy got the mail after school, he saw a strange envelope. It was from his friend Lance. Jeremy opened the envelope. It had a note with a penny taped to it. The note read, " Dear Jeremy, This penny is for you. It is for good luck. Keep it for two days then send it on to another friend and he or she will have good luck, too.
Your friend, Lance."

Jeremy was surprised. He wondered if the penny would really bring him good luck. Jeremy asked his mom if she thought it would work.

Mom said, "I don't think

that a penny can bring you luck. Now, is your bed made? I'm not a maid, you know."

Jeremy went into his room. His bed was made, but he knew that he hadn't done it. Who made his bed? Maybe it was the luck from the penny. He had a hard time thinking that was true.

Later, he went to clean up his mess in the bathroom, and he saw that the bathroom was clean! How had that happened?

He went to put on his new shoes. He hadn't worn his new shoes for a few days because he knew the laces had a knot in them that he hadn't been able to get out. When he saw the laces, the knot was out! He knew that he had not done it. Again, he wondered how it had happened.

That night, he laid in bed thinking about the strange things that had happened that day. Was it the good luck penny? Jeremy couldn't understand it.

The next day at school, Jeremy saw Lance on the playground. Jeremy told him what had happened the day before.

"Oh, I'm glad you got the note. Did it bring you good luck?" said Lance.

"I guess so," said Jeremy. "It sure is strange!"

That day after school, Jeremy wrote a note and taped the penny to it. He sent it to his friend John. Jeremy's older sister, Jean, saw him.

"What are you doing?" Jean asked.

"I'm mailing this penny to John," Jeremy said. He told Jean what had happened the day before.

"I'm sorry to tell you this, but your good luck wasn't because of the penny. I had some extra time yesterday afternoon. I decided to clean up the house. I made your bed and cleaned up the mess in the bathroom," said Jean.

"But what about my shoelace?" Jeremy asked.

"I heard you telling Mom about it a few days ago. She said that she would try to fix it. I knew that she had been busy and hadn't been able to do it, so I did," Jean said.

"Oh. Well, thanks for doing those things for me," said Jeremy.

Jeremy felt a little bit sad. He had wanted to think that the penny had brought him luck, but he knew that things didn't just happen by magic. Still, it had been fun to think that they did for a while.

1. How did Jeremy get the penny?
2. What did Jeremy think that the penny had done for him?
3. How did Jeremy's bed really get made?

The Beet that Beat All of the Others

Clark had a vegetable garden. He was proud of it. Clark grew corn, beets, peas, beans, lettuce, and tomatoes in his garden. All of the vegetables grew big and healthy.

Every year, there was a fair in Clark's town. There were contests of all kinds that people could enter. Clark always entered the largest vegetable contest. The year before, he had brought a huge carrot from his garden. It was big, but not big enough to win the contest. In fact, Clark had

never won the contest, but he kept on trying.

This year, Clark had a huge beet that he was going to enter. It was the biggest beet that he had ever seen. He was sure that it would beat all of the other beets in the contest.

On the day of the fair, Clark took his beet to the vegetable contest booth. He was sure that he would fare well. All of the other beets were much smaller than his.

Clark waited until the judges called for the beets to be shown. Each person brought his or her beet before the judges. Clark was the last one. He came up with his beet. Everyone looked surprised to see such a huge beet.

Clark won the contest. He got a blue ribbon and a check for fifty dollars. Everyone asked Clark what he was going to do with the beet that had beat all of the others.

Clark said, "Why, I am going to cook it and eat it, of course. It should make a meal in itself!"

Everyone laughed and agreed with Clark. Some of the people even offered to join him!

1. Why was Clark proud of his garden?
2. Why did Clark win the contest?
3. What was Clark going to do with his beet?

Dan's Music

Dan's teacher told the class that they would be writing about themselves. She wanted the students to write about something that they did well. Dan wanted to write about his piano playing.

Dan had been taking piano lessons for three years. He hadn't wanted to take the lessons at first, but his mother said that he had to. He didn't want to practice at first. He wanted to play outside instead, but he stuck with it. Dan had gotten good at playing the piano.

Dan had started with easy music at first, so that he could learn how to play the piano. Once he had learned the musical notes and the keys on the piano, he was ready to play harder music. He got better about practicing. His parents were proud of him.

Dan started his paper by writing about how he had begun, not wanting to go to lessons, and not wanting to practice. Then, he told how he had stuck with it, and gotten better. He wrote about how he started to like playing the piano. Dan wrote about how proud his parents were of him and about how they had helped him practice his lessons.

After Dan handed in his paper to his teacher, she was surprised because she had not known that he could play the piano. She asked him if he would play for the rest of the class. He said that he would be glad to.

They used the piano in the music room. Dan played three songs for the class and his teacher. He did a great job. Everyone clapped and wanted him to play some more.

Dan was glad that he had written about his piano playing. He had gotten a chance to show his teacher and his classmates something that he could do well.

1. How did Dan feel about playing the piano at first?
2. What kind of music did Dan start out with at first?
3. What did Dan get to do after he handed his paper in to his teacher?

The Fox and the Antelope

One day, the antelope was out eating grass, just as she did most days. She was very hungry that day, so she was eating a lot. She was minding her own business when along came a fox.

The fox was hungry too, but he didn't eat grass. The antelope knew to stay away from foxes. She went on eating her grass. The fox came close to the antelope. He wanted to talk to her.

"Antelope," said the fox, "you are a very fast runner. You are one of the fastest animals. I think that you can help me."

"Help you?" asked the antelope. "How can I help you, and why should I?"

"I see that you are eating. I am hungry too, but I do not eat grass. I wonder if you could help me to find some food," said the fox.

"I stay out here on the open plains. I don't go in the forest like you do," said the antelope.

"Yes, but you can help me by telling me where the food is. I can find food out here too," said the fox.

"What will I get in return for my help?" asked the antelope.

"I promise that I will leave you and the members of your herd alone," said the fox. "I will not chase any of you."

"If you promise, then I will help you," said the antelope.

She ran down the field a little way, with the fox following behind her. She spotted some food for the fox and stopped. The fox caught up with her.

"Over there is some food for you," said the antelope.

"Thank you," said the fox. He ran over and got his food. He ate it and came back to the antelope.

"Is that enough?" the antelope asked.

"Yes, for now," said the fox. "Will you keep helping me? I will keep my promise to you."

"All right. But you have to do some looking yourself, too. I can't spend all of my time looking for food for you," said the antelope.

"Fine. I can do that," said the fox.

"Good. We wouldn't want you to get lazy," said the antelope.

From then on, the fox and the antelope were friends. They were a very unlikely pair indeed!

1. What was the deal that the fox and the antelope made?
2. Where did the antelope spend most of her time?
3. Did the antelope agree to look for food for the fox all of the time?

Bob's Bike

Bob had been saving his money to buy a new bike. His old bike was too small for him. He couldn't ride it anymore. He had been saving his money for six months, and he had finally gotten a new one.

Bob rode his new bike everywhere. He rode it to school, to the store, to his friends' houses, and to baseball practice. He always remembered to lock up his bike. He knew that new bikes could get stolen very easily.

At home, he kept the bike in the garage. His parents reminded him of it every night. He knew that was important.

One week, his parents went out of town on a trip. Bob's grandma stayed with him. One day after school,

Bob rode his bike to his friend's house. He came home in time for dinner. He left his bike out on the driveway.

Bob ate dinner and did his homework. Then, he went to bed. He never gave a thought to his bike, which was still on the driveway.

The next day, Bob got up and got ready for school. He went out into the garage to get his bike. It wasn't there, of course. Then Bob remembered that he hadn't brought his bike in the night before. Because his parents weren't

there to remind him, he hadn't done it. He opened the garage door, expecting the bike to be gone. Bob was happy to find his bike still sitting on the driveway, right where he had left it. His fear was eased!

As Bob was riding to school, he thought about how blessed he had been this time. He didn't want there to be a "next time".

Bob knew that he needed to remember to bring his bike in himself and not to expect his parents to remind him all of the time. He would be better about remembering.

1. How long did Bob save his money for a new bike?
2. What was the big mistake that Bob made with his bike?
3. What did Bob decide to do at the end?

The Dog Who Dug

The Andersons had a dog that liked to dig. He liked to dig so much that they named him Digger. Digger would dig whenever he got the chance.

Digger dug holes everywhere in the yard. He dug holes by the patio, and he dug holes by the garden. He had even dug in the garden once. Mrs. Anderson had put a fence around the garden after that.

After it rained, Digger had a great time digging holes because the ground was extra soft. He would get all muddy. Then, he would have to stay outside until it was dry. The Andersons were getting tired of having their yard all dug up.

Mr. Anderson decided that it was time to do something about Digger's digging. He went to the pet store and found some special spray. It was supposed to smell bad to dogs and keep them away from wherever it was sprayed. Mr. Anderson sprayed it on all of the places where Digger had dug holes. The Andersons waited and watched to see what would happen.

Digger went over to the spots where he liked to dig. Digger sniffed the spot. He backed away. He went to the next spot and the same thing happened. It seemed that Digger did not like the smell of the spray at all. It had worked! The Andersons were happy.

Mr. Anderson kept the spray in the garage, just in case he needed it again. They never knew where Digger might dig next!

1. Where had Digger dug holes?
2. Why did Mrs. Anderson put a fence around the garden?
3. How did the Andersons stop Digger from digging?

Synonyms

Jim walked through the pretty woods. He loved the beautiful forest. It was quiet sometimes. He liked the silence. He was glad when he got to go hiking. Walking in the woods made Jim happy. He was sad when he had to leave. Leaving made Jim unhappy.

Antonyms

Rebecca liked the cool weather. She didn't like hot weather. She liked wearing a big jacket. It made her feel cozy and warm. Rebecca also liked the soft snow. She didn't like the hard ice, though. She sometimes slipped on it. Rebecca  liked a full cup of cocoa. She didn't like it when her cup was empty.

Homonyms

In one hour, our train will stop here. It will take us to see our friends. We haven't seen them in a week because I had been sick and feeling weak. As we stood and waited, the wind blew. I knew my new blue jacket was not warm enough.

1. What are synonyms?

2. What are antonyms?

3. What are homonyms?

Climbing the Fence

Mrs. Fink had a big
chain-link fence in
her backyard. Her
yard was next to a
busy street. Kids liked
to climb her fence
and walk around the
side of her house to
get to the next street.
It was a shortcut.

Mrs. Fink didn't like people climbing her fence. When
she saw them doing it, she would yell, "Stop! Don't
climb my fence!"

Sometimes, the people would stop. Other times, they
didn't listen and kept climbing. It made Mrs. Fink very

upset. She was afraid that someone would get hurt. Also, she didn't like strange people in her yard. She didn't know what to do.

Her neighbor, Mr. Jones, said that he had the same problem. Then, he had put a wood fence up in front of the chain-link fence. Then people couldn't climb it.

Mrs. Fink thought that this was a good idea. She had a wood fence built in front of the chain–link fence. It worked very well. No one climbed the fence anymore.

Mrs. Fink was happy that she didn't have to yell at anyone anymore. She didn't like to do that. Her wood fence looked so nice that she decided to have the whole yard fenced in with the wood.

1. What did Mrs. Fink do when people would climb her fence?
2. What did Mr. Jones tell Mrs. Fink to do?
3. How did the new fence work?

The Giant Giraffe

George and Greg went to the zoo. It was their favorite place to visit. They both loved the animals. Their favorite animal was the giraffe.

George had read in the newspaper that the zoo had a new giraffe. The zoo had just gotten it from a zoo in another city. There was a picture of the giraffe in the paper. It was huge! It was the tallest giraffe that the zoo had ever had. George couldn't wait to see it. He called Greg and invited him to go to the zoo with him on the weekend to see the new giraffe.

George and Greg went to the zoo on Saturday. There were a lot of other people at the zoo wanting to see the new giraffe also. The giraffe was in a big open place with other animals. A cage would have been too small. The giraffe stood very tall above all

of the other animals. George could see the giraffe's head right away when he got in the door to the zoo.

"Wow!" cried George. "I've never seen an animal so tall. How tall do you think he is, Greg?"

"I don't know, but he's the tallest animal I've ever seen," said Greg.

George and Greg stood there for a long time, just watching the giraffe. It was fun to see him eating leaves off the trees. He had to bend his neck down to reach even the highest trees.

"Let's come back next week," said Greg.

"Yes, I'd like to see if the giraffe grows!" said George.

1. How did George find out about the huge giraffe?
2. When did George and Greg go to see the giraffe?
3. What did the giraffe eat?

A Quilt for the Queen

The queen wanted a new quilt. She lived in a castle that was very cold and her old quilt was worn out. The queen called in Quinn, her best seamstress, to make a new quilt for her.

Quinn got right to work. She got some helpers and they began cutting fabric for the quilt. It took many little pieces of fabric to make the large quilt that the queen wanted.

After the pieces of fabric were cut out, they had to be sewn together. Quinn and her helpers took three days to sew all of the pieces together.

After all of the fabric pieces were sewn together, Quinn sewed a warm layer of cloth to the layer of pieces that were sewn together. The  warm layer was made of soft, thick cloth. That was what would help keep the queen warm.

After that was done, the bottom layer of fabric had to be sewn on to the rest of the quilt. That was the easy part. Quinn just had to cut a piece of fabric the same size as the rest of the quilt. Then she sewed it all around the edges.

The final step was to put some fancy stitches around the inside of the quilt. This was to make the quilt look nice, but it was also to help hold it together.

When this was done, Quinn brought the quilt to the queen.

"It is a very pretty quilt. You have done a fine job, Quinn," said the Queen.

"Thank you. I hope that this quilt will keep you very warm," said Quinn.

1. Why did the queen need a new quilt?
2. What was the first thing that had to be done to make the quilt?
3. What was the last thing that Quinn did to make the quilt?

A Photo of Phillip

John was looking at a photograph. It was an older photo of a man. John didn't know who the man was. He asked his mom.

"That is a photo of your great-uncle, Phillip. He was your grandpa's brother," said John's mom.

"It is a funny photo," said John. "Uncle Phillip is making a funny face." John began to laugh.

"Uncle Phillip liked to do funny things," said Mom. "He was always making us laugh."

John's mom told him about a time when she was a little girl. Uncle Phillip had taken her for a pony ride. After she was done riding, Uncle Phillip had tried to ride the pony, but the pony didn't like him. The pony had bucked Uncle Phillip off. Uncle Phillip hadn't been hurt. Mom laughed and laughed as she told that story.

"I wish that I had known Uncle Phillip," said John. "I know that I would have liked him."

"I'm sure that you would have," said Mom. "He was a lot of fun."

1. Who was Phillip?
2. Why was the photo of Phillip funny?
3. What had Phillip and John's mother done when she was a
   little girl?

Raising the Flags

Sam and Shawn were brothers. It was their job to raise the flags every morning before school. They would get flags out of a special place in the school office. They would unfold the flags carefully and attach them to the rope on the flagpole.

Then, they would pull the rope until the flags were at the top of the flagpole.

After school was over for the day, Sam and Shawn would take the flags down. They would lower the rope until they could reach the flags. Then, they would take the flags off the rope. They surely were careful not to let the flags touch the ground. They would fold the flags in a special way. When they were done folding, the flags would be in the shape of a triangle.

One day, Sam and Shawn were both sick and couldn't come to school. No one thought about who would raise and lower the flags. School started and the flags

were not up. No one was sure why the flags were not up. Then, the school secretary, Mrs. Simpson, remembered that Sam and Shawn's mother had called school that morning and said that the boys were sick and wouldn't be at school that day. Mrs. Simpson called their classroom to get two other students to raise and lower the flags that day.

Rose and Sarah came to the office. Mrs. Simpson showed the girls where the flags were and how to raise and lower the flags on the rope. The girls were happy to take over. They did a good job and enjoyed it. After school, they went outside and took the flags down.

Mrs. Simpson said, "You girls did a great job. Thanks for filling in today."

"We will be glad to do it anytime," said Rose. "It was fun!"

1. What did Sam and Shawn do in the morning before school?

2. What did Sam sand Shawn do after school?

3. Who filled in for Sam and Shawn when they were sick?

Cousin Sue

Cousin Sue liked to go on adventures. She had been to many fun places. She liked to tell everyone about where she had been. Everyone always enjoyed hearing about what she had done.

Sue had been to Africa. She had seen lots of different animals. She told about a time when she had

seen an elephant. The elephant had not been happy to see Sue. She thought that surely she was in trouble. She drove away quickly, so that the elephant wouldn't get any closer to her.

Sue told about a time that she had been to a sugar cane field. The workers there had let her taste a piece of the sugar cane. It was very sweet, but it was very rough. They told her that the cane was what sugar was made from.

Cousin Sue's adventures had taken her to many different places. No one knew where she would go next.

1. What had happened to Cousin Sue in Africa?
2. What had Cousin Sue done in the sugar field?
3. Where do you think Cousin Sue will go next?

The Dog Who Could Fly

Mary had to write a story for her teacher. The teacher said that everyone had to write a story about an imaginary animal. Mary was having a hard time thinking of an imaginary animal.

Mary thought about her story on her way home from school. She didn't think that she had a very good imagination. She was having trouble trying to make up an animal.

When Mary got home, she asked her older sister, Michelle, for ideas. Michelle said, "You don't have to make up an animal. Just think of a real

animal and make it do something that it couldn't do in real life."

"That's a great idea," said Mary. "Thanks, Michelle."

Mary decided to write about a dog. In her story, the dog could fly. He was a super-hero that saved the world from bad things. He was like 'Super Dog'! Mary had a lot of fun writing her story. She liked the way it turned out.

The next day, everyone in Mary's class gave their stories to the teacher. Later on in the day, after the teacher had looked at the stories, she asked some of the students to read their stories to the rest of the class. The teacher chose Mary's story first. Mary proudly got up in front of the class and read her story. It was a funny story. Everyone liked it.

Mary had so much fun writing her story that she decided to write another story just for fun!

1. What did Mary's teacher tell her students to write about?

2. Who gave Mary the idea for her story?

3. What was Mary's story about?

A Crying Baby

Penny's baby sister cried a lot. She was a little baby and couldn't tell anyone what was wrong with her. She would just cry and cry.

Penny would try many things to get her sister to stop crying. She would tickle her, she would play with her, she would make funny faces. The baby would still cry.

One day, Penny's friend, Ann, came home with her after school to visit and stay for dinner. Penny's baby sister had just gotten up from her nap. She should have been happy, but she was crying. Penny tried to make her stop. She made a funny face, but that didn't work.

Ann said, "Let me try. Maybe I can make the baby stop crying."

"You can try, but nothing I do makes her stop," said Penny.

Ann got the baby to sit in her lap. She smiled at the baby. She talked baby talk. She made funny faces and smiled again. Sure enough, the baby stopped crying and laughed. She thought Ann was funny. After that, the baby crawled after Ann all over the house. She and Ann had made friends.

Penny's mom said, "Well, Ann, the next time the baby cries, we'll have to call you!"

1. What did Penny try to do to make the baby stop crying?

2. What did Ann do to make the baby stop crying?

3. Why do you think the baby stopped crying for Ann?

He'll Go, She Won't

Henry loved school. He couldn't wait to go after the summer was over. He liked his teacher and he had many friends in his class. His sister, Janet, was going into kindergarten. She didn't want to go to school.

Janet said, "I'll be scared. I won't know any of the kids."

"You'll meet new friends," said Henry. "Everyone is scared at first. Then, you meet new friends and everything is fine."

"I don't know," said Janet. "It'll all be new. I won't know what to do."

"It'll be okay,' said Henry. "I'll take you to your class on the first day of school. I'll help you meet your new teacher."

"Okay," said Janet.

When the first day of school came, Henry and Janet walked to school together. Janet was still scared. She didn't want to go. When they got to the crosswalk by the school, Janet stopped.

"No, I can't go," she said.

"Yes, you have to," said Henry. "Come on. I'll take you to your class."

They found Janet's classroom. Henry helped Janet meet her teacher. Her name was Miss Simmons. She seemed very nice.

"Hello, Janet," said Miss Simmons. "Please come in. We'll find you something to do until the rest of the class gets here. Thanks, Henry. We'll take it from here."

Janet went with Miss Simmons. She waved good-bye to Henry. As Henry went to his own new classroom, he knew that Janet was going to be fine.

1. Why did Janet not want to go to school?

2. What did Janet do as she and Henry were walking to school?

3. What happened when Janet and Henry got to Janet's class?

The Dance Lessons

Jan wanted to learn to tap dance. Some of her friends were taking lessons and she wanted to also. Her mom signed her up for tap-dance lessons.

At the first lesson, Jan had a hard time. The other girls knew how to do most of the steps. The class was moving fast.

Jan thought to herself, "I can't do this. I shouldn't be here. I don't like it here."

The dance teacher could see that Jan was having trouble. She came over and helped Jan with the steps.

The teacher said, "Please don't get upset. I will help you. These girls have been taking lessons for a while. They already know the steps. You will learn."

Jan said, "I won't be able to do what they do."

"Yes, you will. They didn't know how to do it at first, either. It took time and practice for  them to learn, just like it will for you," said the teacher.

Jan felt a little bit better. She decided that she shouldn't quit. She kept trying. By the end of the lesson, Jan had learned two steps. She thought that maybe she would like tap lessons after all.

Jan learned new things every week. By the end of the first month of lessons, Jan was doing just as well as the other girls. She was glad that she had decided to stay with it and didn't give up.

1. How did Jan feel at her first lesson?
2. How did the teacher help Jan?
3. Did Jan give up, or did she stick with the lessons?

Mark's Poem

Mark liked to write poems. He wrote funny poems, sad poems, poems that rhymed, and poems that didn't rhyme. He had quite a collection of poems that he had written. He kept them in a folder.

Mark decided to write a poem about his favorite food. His favorite food was pizza. He thought about what he could write about pizza. What did he like about pizza? He liked the cheese, the sauce, and the toppings. His favorite kind of pizza was pepperoni. He would write a poem about pepperoni pizza. His poem went like this:

Pepperoni pizza,

It's my favorite food.

Pizza, pizza, pizza, pizza,

Good, good, good!

Mark knew that poems didn't have to rhyme. His poem rhymed a little bit. He showed the poem to his brother, Jacob.

Jacob said, "That is a good poem. You should put it in your folder."

"I will," said Mark. He thought he would start a different folder just for poems about food. He liked lots of foods, so it would be a big folder!

1. Where did Mark keep his poems?
2. What was Mark's food poem about?
3. What did Mark decide to start doing?

Kay's Toys

Kay had lots of toys. She kept them in a box in the closet. Kay had so many toys that she had a hard time finding things in her toy box. She decided that she needed to get rid of some of her toys.

Kay pulled the toy box out of her closet. She looked through it. It was a mess.

"I've got to get rid of some of these toys," Kay thought. "I don't play with all of these toys. Someone else might like them."

Kay had her mom help her sort out her toys. It took a

long time. Kay made two piles of toys; one to keep, and one to give away.

Mom said, "I'm glad to see you getting rid of some of these. They've been around for a long time. Some of them are your baby toys."

"Yes, they've been in my toy box so long that I've forgotten about them," said Kay.

"We've picked a good time to do this," said Mom. "You've made a good choice."

Mom called a truck to come and get the toys. They would be given to children who needed them. Kay was happy to help other children.

1. Where did Kay keep her toys?
2. How did Kay divide up the toys?
3. What did Kay do with her old toys?

Chet's Mud

Chet was a large, happy pig. He lived on a farm in a pen with four other pigs. The other pigs loved to roll around in the mud. They liked being muddy and dirty. Chet didn't like the mud. He liked to be clean and dry.

The other pigs would say, "Let's roll around in the mud! It feels so cool and slippery!"

Chet would say, "No, thank you. I don't like to be muddy. I like to stay dry."

The other pigs would say to one another, "Chet thinks he's so special. It's a shame that Chet doesn't like to have fun as we do.'

Chet sometimes felt badly that he didn't do the things that the other pigs did. He tried, but he just couldn't bring himself to get muddy.

The farmer saw how clean Chet stayed. He said to his helper, "See that pig? He's always clean. It's odd the way that pig doesn't like to get muddy." Chet heard the farmer say that. Was he really odd for not wanting to get dirty?

The next day, Chet decided that he would try the mud. Maybe it wasn't so bad after all. He put one foot in. It felt cool. He put both of his front feet in the mud. Then, he put all four feet in. It felt good! Chet danced all around in the mud. Soon, the other pigs saw Chet and came over to him.

"Hey, Chet," one of the pigs said. "We thought that you didn't like to get muddy!"

"Well, I guess that it's not so bad. It's actually kind of fun!" said Chet.

"We knew that you'd come around sooner or later," said the other pig. "Now you can have fun with us!"

1. Why did Chet not like the mud?
2. What did the farmer say about Chet?
3. How did Chet like the mud in the end?

Let's Have Fun!

Joel and Dennis were two boys who liked to have fun. It was the thing that they liked the best. They tried very hard to have fun.

It wasn't always such a good thing to be that way in school. Joel and Dennis sometimes got in trouble because they were trying too hard to have fun when they were supposed to be doing something else.

At recess, when it was time to come in, Joel and Dennis would say, "Let's have fun! I'm not ready to go in, are you?" Then, they would get into trouble because they were supposed to be lining up to go in.

Sometimes, when Dennis would be at Joel's house and Joel had to do his chores, Dennis would say, "Let's have fun instead!" This would lead to trouble also.

Joel's mom wouldn't let Dennis come over for a while.

One day, the boys pushed this a little bit too far. Joel was supposed to be raking leaves in the front yard. Dennis came by on his bike.

Dennis said, "Let's go have some fun. Your mom won't know that you're gone. I'll help you with the leaves when we get back."

"Okay," said Joel.

The boys went to the park and played and rode their bikes. When they got back, Joel's mom was very upset.

"Joel, not only did I not know where you were, but you were supposed to be raking leaves. Dennis, please go home now," Joel's mom said. "Joel, you will finish raking the leaves. Then, you will go in the house and you will be grounded for two weeks. You will go nowhere unless Dad or I are with you."

"Okay. I'm sorry, Mom," said Joel, as Dennis rode away on his bike. Joel was sorry that he had gotten his mom upset and that he had not done his job.

1. What did the boys do at recess?

2. What did Joel do instead of raking leaves?

3. What happened to Joel when he didn't do his job?

We're Going on a Trip

The Jipp Family was going on a trip. The children were out of school for the summer. Dad and Mom had taken time off work. The family would be gone for two weeks.

The Jipps decided to go to the mountains to stay in a cabin. They would go for hikes in the woods, swim in the nearby lake, and relax. There would be lots of room for their dog to run and play. It would be a great trip.

On the day that the Jipps left, they all helped get the car packed. They would need many things for the trip. They all took lots of shorts, T-shirts, and swimming suits. They left their fancy clothes at home. They took a little bit of food with them in the car for snacks on the way there.

It was a long drive to the cabin. The Jipps played games along the way. They had a contest to see who could count the most license plates from different states. They played a game in which they looked for different letters of the alphabet on signs. Then, they tried to look for different words on the signs. This helped pass the time.

When they got to the cabin, the Jipps unloaded the car. It took a while to carry everything in. Once they were settled, they decided to take a rest. It had been a long trip and they were tired.

The Jipps were looking forward to a fun, relaxing time at the cabin. It was going to be a fun trip!

1. During what season did the Jipps go to the cabin?
2. What did the Jipps do on the way to the cabin?
3. What did the Jipps do once they got to the cabin?

The Pickle Jar

Mark had a jar of pickles. He wanted to eat one. It was a new jar and hadn't been opened.

Mark tried to open the jar. He tried and tried. He couldn't get it open. He tried again, as hard as he could. The jar would not open. His dad had bigger hands, but he wasn't home, so Mark couldn't ask him for help.

Mark really wanted a pickle. "Why do they put these lids on so tightly?" he wondered to himself. "What am I going to do to get this jar open?"

Just then, Mark's mom came into the kitchen.

"What's the matter, Mark?" Mom asked.

"I want a pickle and I can't get this jar open. I tried with all of my strength, but it won't open," said Mark.

"Let me try," said Mom.

She got a towel wet and put it around the lid. She tried to twist the lid. It wouldn't open. She tried again, as hard as she could. No luck. Then, she decided to try something that she had seen her own mother do, years before. She got a table knife from the drawer and hit the edge of the lid with the handle a few times. She tried to open the jar again. This time it worked!

"How did you do that?" Mark asked.

"I hit the lid with the handle of the knife. It must have broken the seal of the jar," said Mom.

"That's a good idea, " said Mark.

"You just make sure that you have a grown-up do it for you," said Mom.

1. What did Mark want to eat?
2. What was the problem in the story?
3. How did Mark's mom help?

Popcorn with a Fork

Cora loved popcorn. It was her favorite snack. She loved making popcorn because it always smelled so good when it was popping. She loved putting the butter and salt on the popcorn. Most of all, she loved eating it.

Cora had tried all different kinds of popcorn. She had tried caramel corn, cheese popcorn, and garlic popcorn. She liked them all. Cora was trying to think of a different way to eat popcorn.

Cora always ate her popcorn with her fingers. That was the way that everyone did it, she thought. She wanted to try something different. Cora thought that she would try using a fork to eat her popcorn.

Cora made a batch of popcorn and got a fork out of

the drawer. She put the popcorn into a bowl. She stuck the fork into the popcorn. It didn't go through very well, but she was going to try. She got a piece of the popcorn on her fork. She ate it. So far, so good. Cora found that she had to eat the popcorn one piece at a time if she used the fork.

It took Cora a long time to eat the popcorn using the fork. It was fun for a while, but it wasn't something she wanted to do all of the time.

Cora decided that she would go back to eating popcorn with her fingers. It was more fun, and it took less time. Cora understood why popcorn was made to be a finger food.

1. Why did Cora want to eat popcorn with a fork?
2. Did Cora like eating the popcorn with a fork?
3. What did Cora decide about eating popcorn with a fork?

The Horse in the Barn

Zeb was a big brown horse. He lived on a farm with many other animals. Zeb had his own stall in the red barn. He was happy on the farm.

The farmer who owned Zeb liked to ride him often. The farmer would put Zeb's blanket and saddle on him and they would take off, riding fast into the fields. Zeb loved to run fast. He always looked forward to going riding with the farmer.

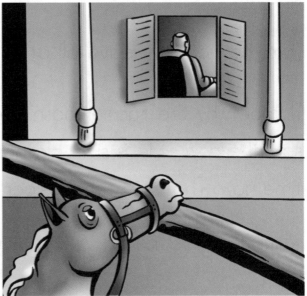

Several weeks went by, and Zeb was thinking that it had been a long time since he and the farmer had gone riding. Zeb wondered why the farmer hadn't been by to take him riding. Zeb hadn't even seen the farmer in a long time.

One day, Zeb heard some of the other animals talking about why the farmer had not been around. Only the farm helper had come to feed them and clean out the pens and stalls. They were all wondering what was wrong.

"Maybe he went to live somewhere else," said the goose.

"No, he wouldn't leave all of us here," said the pig.

"I know why the farmer hasn't been around to see us," said the cow. "He is sick. He has been sick for some time now. That's why the helper has been feeding us."

"Oh, the poor farmer," said Zeb. "What can we do for him?"

"There is nothing we can do, except to wait for him to get better," said the cow.

So, the animals waited and waited. Zeb missed going riding. He spent the days eating grass in the field and resting in his stall.

Then one day, Zeb saw the geese running around and honking loudly.

"What is going on?" Zeb asked the cow.

"The farmer is back. He has gotten better," said the cow.

"Maybe we can go riding today!" Zeb said to the cow.

Sure enough, the farmer came right over to Zeb. "How's my old Zeb?" the farmer asked. "Want to go riding today?"

Zeb pranced around. He was so happy. The farmer got his saddle and put it on Zeb. Then, off they went! It was the best ride they had ever had. They were gone almost all day. Zeb couldn't remember a time when he had been happier.

1. Where did Zeb live?

2. What did Zeb and the farmer like to do?

3. Why didn't the farmer come around for a while?

The Office Clerk

Fern was an office clerk. It was her job to answer the phone, do the filing, and type letters. She liked her job and was very good at it.

Many people came into the office. Fern always greeted the people and told them where they needed to go, or whom they needed to see to get what they needed.

One day, the office was very busy. There were a lot of people there that day. Everyone needed something different. Fern was by herself that day, because the other lady who helped Fern was sick that day.

It seemed as if Fern couldn't please anyone. When she told one person something, another person wanted something else. Whatever she told them, it was wrong.

She had never had a day like that before. Everything had always gone well in the office.

Fern's boss, Mrs. Shaw, came out of her office many times to see what was going on.

Fern said, "I don't know why things are going wrong today. Nobody is happy with the things that I am telling them. This never happens."

"I know, Fern. You are a good clerk. I will try to get the people in and out of my office faster. Maybe that will help you out," said Mrs. Shaw.

From then on, the day seemed to go better. Mrs.

Shaw took care of the people in her office faster, and more people got in and out quicker. By the end of the day, Fern was ready to go home.

"This has been a hard day," Fern told Mrs. Shaw. "I hope that we don't have a day like this again!"

"So do I," said Mrs. Shaw.

1. What was Fern's job?
2. Who was Fern's boss?
3. Why was Fern having a bad day?

The Girl with the Dirty Face

Shirley always had a dirty face. It got dirty because she liked to play outside. She liked to play in the sand and dirt. Shirley made things out of the dirt. She dug in the dirt and made tunnels in it. She also made things out of the sand. She would add water to the dirt and sand and make sand and dirt houses and castles.

Shirley had a sandbox in her backyard. There was also an area of the backyard that had dirt. Those were her favorite places to play. She played out there all day long. She got very dirty.

Shirley's mother would call her when it was time to come in to eat lunch or supper. Mother would always say, "Shirley, go wash your hands and face. You are very dirty."

Shirley would go wash. She would eat, and then she would go back out to play.

Once, Shirley and her mother were going to a wedding. The wedding was at night. Shirley had played in the dirt and sand all day, as usual. Mother had called her in to get ready for the wedding. Shirley had gone into the bathroom to wash her hands and face. On the way to the bathroom, Shirley had seen her dog. She played with her dog. Mom came over and

told Shirley that she needed to get dressed because they were getting ready to leave for the wedding. Shirley went into her room and put on her best dress. Mom came to Shirley's room.

"Shirley! Look at your face and hands!" Mother cried. "You didn't wash! Please go do it now, and hurry!"

Shirley remembered that she had played with her dog instead of washing her hands and face. She looked at her face in the bathroom mirror. She was very dirty! She washed quickly and went out to the car.

"That is much better," said Mother. "You almost went to the wedding with a dirty face!"

1. Where did Shirley like to play?
2. What happened to Shirley when she played?
3. What did Shirley almost do?

The Boy Who Had to be First

Nathan was a boy who liked to be the best at everything. He always wanted to be first. He wanted to be first in line, first when he ran in a race, and first to the supper table.

Nathan's parents tried to get him to see that he didn't always have to be first at everything. They wanted him to understand that sometimes it's all right to be second or third. Nathan didn't want to listen.

One day at school, Nathan's class was at PE. The teacher told the class that they were going to have a race. The boys would race against the boys and the girls would race against the girls. The boys raced first. The teacher lined them up. The teacher told the boys that when he clapped his hands, it would be the signal to go.

Nathan listened carefully for the teacher to clap his hands. Clap! The boys were off and running. They ran around the field, around the swings and the basketball poles. The home stretch was down the other side of the field. Nathan was in the lead. He ran as fast as he could. After a while, there was another boy gaining on him. Soon, Nathan and the other boy were right next to each other. Nathan couldn't let the other boy win. Nathan ran as fast as he could go. He couldn't run any faster. The other boy was starting to get ahead.

Soon, Nathan was behind, in second place. The other boy was ahead for the home stretch. In the end, the other boy won the race.

Everyone cheered and crowded around the other boy. Nathan was upset. The teacher went over to him.

"Nathan, you did a great job. You almost won the race!" said the teacher.

"Yes, but I didn't win," said Nathan.

"Maybe it's time to go over and tell the winner that you are happy for him," said the teacher. "You need to be a good loser too, you know."

"I never thought of it that way," said Nathan. "I will go over and tell him that I am happy for him."

"Good job," said the teacher. "Learning a lesson is almost better than winning."

1. What did Nathan always want to be?

2. What happened at the end of the race?

3. What did Nathan learn?

The Nice Nurse

Mrs. Turner was a school nurse. She was very nice. She took good care of the children at the school. All of the children loved her.

Mrs. Turner did many different things for the children. She took their temperatures, looked at their ears and throats, and checked their eyes every year to see if anyone needed glasses.

If a student got hurt on the playground, he or she would go to see Mrs. Turner and she would fix them up. She would put a bandage on a cut or first aid cream on a sting.

Sometimes, Mrs. Turner's office was very busy. One winter, there were lots of colds going around. Many children were getting sick. If a student felt badly in class, he or she went to Mrs. Turner's office. She would let the student rest on one of the cots in her office, or she would call a parent to come and get the student.

Even the teachers had Mrs. Turner take care of them, sometimes. If a teacher got sick at school, Mrs. Turner could give a teacher some medicine or take their temperature.

All of the people at the school thought that having Mrs. Turner was a blessing. She was a very special person.

1. What was Mrs. Turner's job?
2. What did Mrs. Turner check every year?
3. Who else, besides students, did Mrs. Turner take care of?

Carol's Journal

Carol kept a journal. She wrote in it every day. Carol wrote all of her feelings and thoughts in her journal. She wrote down the things that she did every day.

Carol kept her journal in a special place in the desk in her room. She didn't want anyone to find it and read it. It was her own private book.

One day, she had her friend, Jean, over after school. Carol and Jean were playing in Carol's room. Carol had left her journal out that morning and had forgotten to put it away. Jean saw it.

"What is that?" asked Jean.

"That is my journal," said Carol.

"What is a journal?" asked Jean.

"It's a book where I write down my thoughts and feelings. I also write down the things that I do each day," said Carol. "Can I read it?" asked Jean.

"No, I don't let anyone read it. It's private," said Carol.

"Is there anything about me in it?" asked Jean.

"I don't think so," said Carol.

"Will you write about what we do today?" asked Jean.

"Yes, I will. I will write about the fun we are having and that you are my good friend," said Carol.

"I think I will start my own journal when I get home," said Jean.

"It is fun to have. When I am older, I will read it and remember all of the fun I had," said Carol.

1. What is a journal?
2. Where did Carol keep her journal?
3. What will Carol do with her journal when she is older?

Repacking the Backpack

Jill had to carry a backpack to school. She had a lot of books and papers to take with her. She always had a lot of homework.

The backpack was heavy. Jill had a hard time carrying it. She would pack it in the morning and repack it in the afternoon to go home after school.

One day after school, Jill was getting ready to go home. She took all of the books that she needed to take home with her out of her locker. She started packing them into her backpack. Jill had more homework than usual, so

she had more books to carry that day. She put three books in and then four. When she tried to put the fifth book in the backpack, it wouldn't fit. She took out the folders and tried to put the book in. It still wouldn't fit. She took everything out and started to repack the backpack.

Jill tried to reload the books into the backpack. Everything just would not fit in at once. She looked at everything that she had. She decided that she needed everything, so she would have to carry one or two of the books outside of the backpack. She repacked all of the books and folders. She zipped up the backpack. She put the backpack on and gathered up the rest of the books.

It was a hard trip home that day. Jill was tired when she got there. She knew that she would have to

repack everything in the morning. She decided that she needed a bigger backpack.

1. Why was Jill's backpack heavy?
2. Why did Jill have to repack her backpack?
3. How did Jill get all of her books home?

The Unhappy Boy

Jack was unhappy. He was having a bad day. He had lost his favorite toy. He had been late for school. His brother had eaten all of his favorite cereal.

When Jack got to school, he couldn't unbutton his coat. His teacher had to help him. When he unpacked his backpack, everything fell out at once and made a mess on the floor.

At recess, Jack's belt came unbuckled. His friend had to tell him because Jack hadn't seen it. Then, his shoes kept coming untied.

When Jack got home, he told his mom about his bad day. She felt sorry for him.

"I have a surprise for you. I had been saving it for your birthday, but I think that you need it now," said Jack's mom.

She left the room for a minute and came back with a box wrapped in bright wrapping paper. Jack was excited.

"This is for me? What is it?" Jack asked.

"Open it and find out," said Mom.

Jack unwrapped the package. It was a new toy

race car, the one that he had been wanting. Jack was very happy.

"Thanks, Mom. You were nice to give this to me today," said Jack.

"Maybe the day hasn't been so bad after all," said Mom.

1. Why was Jack having a bad day?
2. What did Jack's mom do to make his day better?
3. How did Jack's day turn out?

Kyle Dislikes his Food

Kyle was what his parents called a "picky eater." He wouldn't eat very many foods. He disliked meat. He disliked vegetables. His parents were getting upset.

At suppertime, Kyle would turn his nose up at most of the food. He would say, "I dislike that food. May I have something else, please?"

Mom would say, "No. You can eat what we are eating."

Often, Kyle would not eat more than two or three bites. Kyle's parents wondered how he didn't get hungry all of the time. They were displeased because he wasn't getting enough food.

Kyle and his parents went to a restaurant one night for supper. Kyle's parents were afraid that Kyle would dislike everything on the menu. Kyle looked at the menu. He was displeased at what he saw.

"I don't like anything on here," said Kyle.

"Don't order anything then," said Mom.

"Okay," said Kyle.

Kyle's parents ordered their meals. When their food came, they began eating. Kyle watched them for a while. He was hungry.

Kyle's dad said, "Would you like a bite of my steak?"

Kyle looked at the steak. He had never had steak before. He had just guessed that he wouldn't like it.

"Well, I guess that I'll try it," Kyle said.

Dad cut a small piece and put it on Kyle's empty plate. Kyle put the piece in his mouth. He chewed it. He discovered that he liked it!

"May I have another piece? I think I like it," said Kyle.

"Sure," said Dad. "Would you like to order some steak?"

"Yes, and a baked potato," said Kyle.

"Wow! You must be really hungry," said Mom.

"I discovered that I like steak," said Kyle.

Kyle's dad called the waitress over and ordered Kyle a steak and a baked potato.

Mom said, "I am so glad that you are trying a new food."

Kyle said, "Maybe I won't be so picky anymore and will start trying more new things!"

1. Why were Kyle's parents displeased?
2. Why didn't Kyle order anything at the restaurant at first?
3. What did Kyle discover about the steak?

Why Play a Xylophone?

Ken played the xylophone in the high school band. He had fun playing it. It was an interesting instrument. He was the only one in the band who knew how to play it.

Ken was very good at playing the xylophone. The band director would often let Ken play parts by himself when the band was performing. Ken's high school band was famous in their area because Ken was so good.

Ken started taking xylophone lessons when he was ten years old. Some of the other kids thought that Ken was odd because he wanted to learn to play such a different instrument.

"Why play a xylophone?" they would ask Ken.

Ken would tell them, "Because it's fun!"

Ken's band teacher had to look for another person to teach Ken to play the xylophone because the band teacher didn't know anything about it.

When Ken's band teacher found someone to teach Ken how to play the xylophone, he thought he would learn how to play the xylophone, too. Ken's band teacher was learning something also.

Ken's parents were proud of him. They had wondered why Ken wanted to play the xylophone at first, but when they saw how much he wanted to learn, they helped him practice his lessons.

Ken's friends were helpful, too. They listened while Ken played the songs that he had to learn.

Ken's xylophone playing made everyone happy. It was a fun instrument to watch and to listen to.

1. Why was Ken's high school band famous?

2. When did Ken start taking xylophone lessons?

3. How did Ken's friends help him with his lessons?

The Man Who Fixed Cars

Max's dad fixed cars. He did it at their house. Max's dad always had a lot of cars to fix. He did a good job fixing cars.

Max's dad had many tools that he used to fix cars. He had lots of different wrenches, each a different size. He had many screwdrivers, each of them a different size. Some of them had different kinds of heads on them to fit different things.

Max's dad kept most of his tools in special toolboxes. He had one toolbox just for the wrenches. Max liked to look at all of the tools. He thought they were fun. Max thought that, one day, he might fix cars just like his dad.

Max's dad let him stay in the garage while he fixed

the cars. It was dirty work. Dad had special hand cleaner that was just for greasy hands. It always got his hands clean, even when they were black with dirt and grease. Sometimes, Max had to use the hand cleaner, too, because he had touched dirty car parts.

For his birthday, Max got a little toolbox filled with real tools. Max's dad said that he would start teaching Max about fixing cars. Max could hardly wait!

1. What did Max's dad do for a living?
2. Where did Max's dad keep his tools?
3. Why did Dad have a special hand cleaner?

The Alphabet

Joann's little brother, Jacob, was learning the letters of the alphabet in preschool. Since Joann was in fifth grade, she knew the alphabet well. She liked to help Jacob learn it.

At first, Jacob knew the letters up to the letter "g". After that, he had trouble remembering the letters. Joann would play little games with him.

One game that they liked to play was one where Joann said a letter and Jacob wrote it. She would say the letters in

alphabetical order. Jacob sometimes wrote the letters backward, but Joann helped him make the letters the right way.

Soon, Jacob knew the letters up to the letter "m". He was proud of himself. His teachers were very impressed. Jacob told his teachers that his sister had been helping him at home. He liked to sing the alphabet song for his teachers.

It wasn't too much longer before Jacob was able to write all of the letters of the alphabet in order. Joann had him practice every day. When Jacob went to kindergarten the following year, he already knew all of his letters.

1. What did Joann help Jacob with?
2. What did Jacob like to do for his teachers?
3. What did Jacob know when he went to kindergarten?

The Class in Alphabetical Order

Miss Rhodes liked to have her class seated in alphabetical order by first names. It helped her to learn their names faster. The students whose first names started with letters at the beginning of the alphabet sat in the front. The students whose first names started with letters in the middle of the alphabet sat in the middle. The students whose names started with letters at the end of the alphabet sat in the back. After two months, they switched. Those who had been in the back went to the front, and those who had been in the front went to the back.

Some of the students' names started with the same letter. In that case, Miss Rhodes had to go to the second letter of their names. Miss Rhodes had three students whose names started with S: Susan, Stan, and

Sam. Sam was first, Stan was second, and Susan was third.

Miss Rhodes had two students whose names started with W: William and Wesley. Wesley was first and William was second.

Miss Rhodes' way of seating her students helped the students learn alphabetical order. They always knew what letter would come next because they could look at the names of the people in front of them or behind them.

1. Why did Miss Rhodes like to seat her students in alphabetical order?
2. Did the students sit the same way all year long?
3. What did Miss Rhodes do if she had students whose names began with the same letter?

Martha's Dresses

Martha liked to wear dresses. She wore a dress all of the time. She owned two pairs of pants, but she never wore them. Martha liked the way she looked in dresses.

Every time Martha had a birthday, she got dresses. For Christmas, she got dresses. Everyone knew that Martha liked dresses. Martha had many, many dresses.

Martha's friend, Julie, couldn't believe how many dresses Martha had. Her closet was full of them.

"Don't you like anything else but dresses?" Julie asked.

"Yes, but dresses are my favorite thing," said Martha.

"My goodness, you have so many!" Julie said.

"I like my dresses," said Martha.

Martha kept on liking dresses more than anything until one day, when she went to the eye doctor. Martha found out that she needed glasses. She picked out one pair of glasses. They had pink frames. She loved them and wore them every day, as she was supposed to.

After that, Martha decided that glasses would be her favorite thing. She began asking for glasses for her birthday and Christmas. Martha wanted to collect glasses the way that she had collected dresses.

Martha's mother said, "Martha, glasses cost much more money than dresses do. You can only have one pair of glasses."

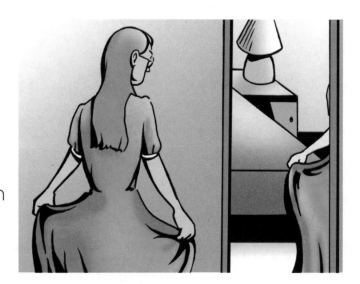

Martha decided that she would go back to liking dresses the best.

1. Why did Martha like dresses so much?
2. What did Martha want to collect instead of dresses?
3. What did Martha's mother say about the other thing that Martha wanted to collect?

Boxes of Books

Matt's grandparents were cleaning out their attic. They were getting ready to move to a new house. They had lived in their old house for many years and had lots of things in their attic.

Matt was helping his grandparents clean out the attic. He was finding many interesting things. He found old pictures of his family and old clothes. He found old toys and shoes. The things that he liked finding the best were the boxes of old books.

Matt sat down and began going through the boxes. He found old school books that belonged to his grandpa. He found an old Bible that his grandma had owned as a little girl. It had her name on the inside of the cover. As Matt was looking through one of the other boxes, he found books that had belonged to his

dad when he was a little boy. They were old storybooks about animals and toys that talked. One of the books had writing in it that looked as if a child had written in it when he wasn't supposed to.

Matt sat and looked in the boxes for a long time. He put some of the books in a box to keep for himself.

Grandpa had said that he could keep whatever he wanted to.

Matt found many treasures in the boxes of books that day.

1. What were Matt's grandparents doing?
2. What were some of the things that Matt found?
3. What did Matt like the best?

Rush Washes the Dishes

Rush's mother told him to wash the supper dishes. He had never washed dishes before. He wasn't sure what to do.

Mother said, "Fill the sink with hot water and squeeze a little bit of dish soap into the water. Then start washing!"

Rush thought that sounded easy enough. He filled the kitchen sink with hot water. As the water was going into the sink, he squeezed some dish soap into the stream of water. That made lots of bubbles in the water.

Rush started with the glasses. He had seen Mother do it that way. He washed all of the glasses. Then, he washed the forks and spoons. Next, he washed the plates and bowls. Last, he washed the pots and pans. When all of the dishes were in the other sink to dry, he thought that he was done.

Mother came into the kitchen to see how Rush had done.

"My, you were done quickly," Mother said. "Let's see how well you did."

Mother looked at the glasses. Then, she looked at the plates, bowls, forks, and spoons.

"Well, these look very nice. You did a good job. After the dishes dry, you can put them away," Mother said.

Rush decided that he liked to wash the dishes. It was his job from then on.

1. How did Rush start washing the dishes?
2. How did Rush know what dishes to start with?
3. How did Rush feel about washing the dishes?

Fresh Peaches

Gloria bought some fresh peaches at the market. Peaches were her favorite fruit. She ate them every day that she could.

Gloria liked fresh peaches on many things. She ate them on ice cream, cake, custard, pie, and even cookies.

The peaches that she bought were very good. They were nicely ripe. She put them out on the kitchen counter. She ate just one, even though she wanted to eat two or more. Gloria ate the peach quickly. It tasted so good that she just couldn't eat it slowly.

She looked at the rest of the peaches sitting on the counter. She thought she would have just one more. She tried to eat that one more slowly. After she had eaten that one, another one sounded good. Soon, Gloria had eaten almost all of the peaches. All of a sudden, she didn't feel well.

Gloria lay down on the couch. Her stomach was feeling sick.

Gloria's mom came in to see what was wrong.

"I don't feel well," said Gloria.

"Why not?" said her mother.

"I think I ate too many peaches. I ate four of them," said Gloria.

"Yes, that was too many. You will feel better in a while, but you should rest for now," said Gloria's mother. "Let me know if you need anything."

"I surely don't need any peaches!" said Gloria.

Her mother laughed at that. "No, you don't!" she said.

1. What did Gloria like to put peaches on?
2. How many peaches did Gloria eat?
3. Why was Gloria feeling sick?

The Monkeys

The monkeys at the zoo are fun to watch. They do funny things. They run all over the place. It is fun to watch them climb on ropes and trees.

Lucy and her sister, Mary, liked to watch the monkeys at the zoo. They stood and watched the monkeys for a long time.

Lucy said, "See how that monkey plays? He likes to be by himself. The others like to play with each other."

Mary said, "Yes, that monkey plays

alone a lot. He stays over in the corner."

The zookeepers brought in trays of food for the monkeys. The monkeys were messy eaters. The food went everywhere. Lucy thought that more food went on the ground than got eaten by the monkeys.

Lucy and Mary looked forward to the days that they got to go to the zoo and see the monkeys. Those days were always fun.

1. What did Lucy and Mary like to watch at the zoo?
2. Who brought the trays of food?
3. What kind of eaters were the monkeys?

The Children and the Geese

Frank and his friends liked to visit the park by their house. The park had a small lake. Some geese lived at the lake. They were pretty to look at.

Frank and his friend, Mike, went to the park one day to fish in the lake. They brought their fishing poles and some worms for bait. They found a good fishing spot

and got their poles ready. They put their fishing lines in the water and sat down to wait for the fish to bite. It was hot, so they took their shoes off and put their feet in the water.

Soon, the geese started to come over to where Frank and Mike were fishing. The boys didn't think anything of it. The geese had never bothered them before. They kept on fishing. The geese got closer. The biggest goose started honking at the boys.

"What is wrong with that goose?" asked Frank.

"Maybe we are in their spot," said Mike.

The boys moved to another spot on the side of the lake and sat down to fish again. The geese started to come close to the boys again. The biggest goose started to flap her wings. She started to run at the boys. She ran straight at Frank. Even though he didn't have any shoes on, Frank ran from the goose.

"What is wrong with this crazy goose?" Frank cried.

"Maybe these geese don't like children," said Mike.

"Let's get out of here!" cried Frank. "Grab our stuff and let's go!"

The boys ran away from the lake. They were glad to be away from the geese.

"I can't believe those geese," said Frank.

"Yes, I guess we won't go fishing there again," said Mike.

1. What did the geese do to Frank and Mike?
2. Why weren't Frank and Mike scared of the geese at first?
3. Why did Mike think the goose was after Frank?

Moose in Alaska

Jay lived in Alaska. There were many animals living near his house. He lived near a forest.

Jay saw animals almost every day when he went outside. It was summer, so the animals were out eating all of the time. Jay could stand in his yard and see the animals.

The animals that Jay really liked were the moose. The moose had such funny looking antlers. The antlers were curvy and curly. The female moose did not have antlers.

The baby moose were cute. Their legs were long and skinny.

Their coats were light brown. Some of the babies had little spots on their coats. The spots would go away when the babies got older.

The male moose were usually alone. They were a little bit scary to Jay because they were so big. The female moose were usually together, or had their babies with them.

Jay liked living in Alaska, even if it was cold and dark for much of the year. He liked it because he got to see such interesting animals.

1. Where did Jay live?
2. What did the baby moose look like?
3. Why was Jay scared of the male moose?

John's Ball

John liked to play ball. He liked all different kinds of games that were played with balls. He liked baseball, soccer, tennis, kickball, and football. His favorite was soccer.

John was on a soccer team. When he went to practice, he liked to take his own soccer ball to practice with. He would come early and practice kicking the ball or making goals.

Some of the other kids on the team liked to come to practice early, too. They also liked to practice with John's ball. He didn't mind letting them use it.

One time, John was practicing before a soccer game and was kicking the ball around. There was a dog nearby that was not on a leash. The dog was looking at John. All of a sudden, the dog ran over to John and took John's ball! The dog grabbed John's ball in his teeth and ran with it.

John chased the dog, but the dog was too fast. They ran all over the soccer field. Some of John's friends ran to help him to catch the dog. The kids all chased the dog into one of the soccer goals.

John ran over to the dog and grabbed his ball out of the dog's mouth. The dog jumped up and down, as if he wanted to play.

"That dog wants to play," shouted one of the kids.

"I don't want my ball to get popped," said John. He looked at his ball. It had a small hole in it, and the air was leaking out. John thought that maybe he could patch the hole when he got home.

Soon, the soccer game started. The dog sat and watched the kids play soccer. After that, the dog came to all of the soccer games that were played at the park. He became the soccer mascot!

1. What game did John play?

2. What happened to John's ball?

3. What did the dog want?

Josh's Hat

Carl and Josh were friends. Carl wanted to wear Josh's baseball hat. Josh said that Carl could wear the hat. Carl wore the hat home. The next day, Carl wore the hat to school.

He had to take it off in class, so he put the hat in his desk. When he put the hat on for recess, it looked a little crushed. Carl pushed the hat out where it had caved in and it was fine.

Josh saw Carl wearing his hat at recess.

Josh said, "I hope you're taking care of my hat."

Carl said, "Yes, I'm taking good care of your hat. I like wearing it."

Bob came by and said, "Say, isn't that Josh's hat?"

Carl said, "Yes, it's Josh's hat. He is letting me wear it today."

Just then, Will ran by and took the hat off Carl's head. Will ran away with the hat. Carl ran after him.

Carl shouted, "Give me that hat! It's Josh's hat, not mine!"

Carl chased Will all around the playground. Finally, Carl caught Will over by the slide.

"Why did you do that? Carl asked Will.

"For fun," Will said. "It was just a joke."

Carl went over to Josh and gave him his hat back.

"Here is your hat back," said Carl.

"Why?" asked Josh.

"I guess I've worn it long enough. I don't want anything else to happen to it," said Carl.

"Thanks for taking care of it," said Josh.

1. What happened to Josh's hat in Carl's desk?
2. What happened to Josh's hat at recess?
3. Why did Carl give the hat back to Josh?

The Biggest Nap

Jess didn't sleep well on Sunday night. She had to get up early for school the next morning. She was tired. She didn't want to get up on Monday morning.

All day at school, Jess had a hard time staying awake. Her teacher kept having to remind her to keep her head off her desk. At recess, Jess didn't feel like playing. She just wanted to sit on the bench.

At lunch, Jess hardly ate anything. She was too tired to eat her food. She gave most of her lunch to her friend, Freddie.

Jess couldn't wait to get home. The ride on the school bus seemed to take forever. When Jess finally got home, she went and lay down on the couch. She wanted to take a nap. Just as she was falling asleep, her mom came into the room.

"Jess, I know you're tired, but if you sleep now, you might not sleep tonight," said Mom.

"Yes, I will," said Jess. "As tired as I am, I might sleep until next week!

"All right. I'll wake you for dinner," said Mom.

Jess went right to sleep. She slept until Mom came and woke her up for dinner.

At dinner, Jess's dad said, "You had the biggest nap I've ever seen. I hope you sleep tonight when it's time for bed."

"Oh, I will," said Jess. "No problem. I am still tired. I'm going to bed right after dinner."

When Jess was finished with dinner, she went to bed. All of that napping hadn't kept her from sleeping at bedtime. She took the biggest nap of all that night when she went to bed.

1. Why was Jess so tired on Monday?
2. How did Jess feel at recess?
3. When did Jess take the biggest nap of all?

Ryan's Letter

Ryan wanted to write a
letter to his friend,
Jason. Jason had lived
next door for three
years. They had been
best friends. Then,
Jason's dad had gotten
a job in another town
and Jason's family had

to move. Ryan missed Jason a lot.

Ryan sat down to write his letter. First, he wrote the
day, month, and year. Next, he wrote a greeting. His
greeting said, "Dear Jason." Ryan then wrote about all
of the things that he had been doing. He wrote about
school and the friends that he and Jason had

together. Ryan wrote about things that were happening in the neighborhood and at the church that he and Jason had both gone to. Ryan asked Jason what he had been doing. Ryan asked Jason if he had made any new friends yet.

For the closing, Ryan wrote, "Your friend." Then, Ryan wrote his name. Ryan put the letter in an envelope and put a stamp on it. He put it in the mailbox to be mailed.

Ryan missed having Jason there, but writing to him made Ryan feel better. Ryan hoped that Jason liked his new home and that he had made many new friends.

1. What are the five parts of a friendly letter?
2. What did Ryan write for his greeting?
3. What did Ryan write for his closing?

Saving Money

June had jobs at home that she had to do. She had to set the table for dinner, keep her room clean, take out the trash, and sweep the kitchen floor. If she did all of her jobs, her parents paid her every week.

June was saving her money. She kept a little of the money to spend on things that she needed, but the rest went into the bank to be saved. June was saving her money for the time when she and her family would take a vacation. She wanted to be able to buy things and do special activities on vacation. June also wanted to buy some new clothes with her money.

June's mom told her that they would be taking a vacation in the summer. June was glad that she had been saving her money. June and her family were going to be riding on an airplane when they went on vacation. June was looking forward to that because she had never done that before. They would be visiting June's grandmother in another state. They would be going to some parks and going to the beach a few times. They would also be going shopping.

June was glad that her parents had taught her that saving money was a good idea. She liked having money of her own.

1. What were June's jobs?
2. Where did June put the money that she saved every week?
3. What would June's family be doing on their vacation?

The Synonym Story

Julie's teacher was teaching the class about synonyms. She told her students to write a story with as many synonyms as they could think of. The student who had the most synonyms in his or her story would get a prize. Julie was sure that she would win.

She had trouble thinking of a story that would make sense and have a lot of synonyms. After a while, she had some ideas. Here is her story:

Once, there was a trash man. His job was to drive his truck around and pick up garbage. His job made him happy. He was glad to have his job. He was quick about doing his job. He made fast work of it.

The trash man had a large area to cover.

His job was big. Sometimes, his truck got heavy because the trash had so much weight. One time, he was sick and couldn't do his job. Another man had to do the work when the trash man was ill.

The trash man's friend asked him why he wanted to do such a messy job. The trash man said, "It's a dirty job, but somebody has to do it!"

Julie's teacher gave her the prize. Her teacher said, "Julie, you win the prize. I counted seven pairs of synonyms. That was the most out of the whole class."

Julie got a bookmark and a poetry book for her prize. Julie had enjoyed writing the story so much that she decided to write another one!

1. What was the writing contest in Julie's class about?

2. What was Julie's story about?

3. What was Julie's prize?

The Girl Who Frowned

Emily was a girl who frowned. No one could get her to smile. Nobody was sure why she was unhappy. The other kids at school tried to get her to smile and be happy.

One boy tried to tell Emily some jokes to make her smile. She didn't think the jokes were funny and she still frowned. A girl tried to tickle Emily. That didn't work

either. Emily still frowned. Another boy tried making funny faces. Emily still didn't smile.

One day, there was a new boy in Emily's class at school. His name was Thomas. Thomas smiled a lot. He seemed to be a very happy person. At recess, Thomas saw that Emily was frowning.

"Why are you frowning so much?" Thomas asked Emily.

"That is just what I do," said Emily.

"You should smile and be happy," said Thomas. "I'll bet that I can make you laugh instead of frown."

"I don't think so," said Emily.

"Let me try,' said Thomas.

"Okay, but no one else has been able to," said Emily.

Thomas tried talking in a silly way. Emily didn't laugh.

He tried walking in a funny way. Emily didn't think that was funny either. He tried telling Emily a silly joke. That didn't work.

Just then, the bell rang to go in for recess. Thomas and Emily ran to get a drink of water. As Thomas was pushing the button for the water and was leaning down to get a drink, the water squirted up high in the air and got Thomas all over his face. His face got all wet! Emily laughed and laughed. She thought this was so funny! Everyone stopped what they were doing and listened to Emily laugh. No one had ever heard her laugh before.

"Thomas, I'm sorry, but that was so funny!" Emily cried.

"I'm glad I could make you laugh," said Thomas. "Now, will someone please get me a paper towel?"

1. Did anyone know why Emily never smiled?

2. What did Thomas try doing to make Emily laugh?

3. What finally got Emily to laugh?

Two to Sea

Adam and Alexa loved the ocean and the beach. They went there every chance that they got. They spent most of their summer vacations at the beach.

Adam and Alexa liked the animals that lived in the sea and on the beach area. They looked for crabs on the sand and collected shells. They watched for whales. They looked out at the blue water. They smelled the ocean winds as they blew.

Once, Adam and Alexa got to go fishing out on the sea. Their mom and dad rented a boat and they all went out on the ocean. It was fun to go fishing on the ocean. Some of the fish were huge! Adam caught a tuna that was two feet long! Alexa caught a sailfish that was quite long also.

The only bad thing that happened that day was when Alexa hurt her heel on the side of the boat. It would take a few days to heal. She still had fun.

Adam and Alexa still had more things that they wanted to see at the sea. There were always new things to discover. Mom and Dad said that they would come back again at the end of the summer for another visit to the ocean.

1. What did Adam and Alexa like about the beach and the ocean?
2. What special thing did Adam and Alexa get to do once?
3. What was the bad thing that happened to Alexa?

Ron's Poem

Ron was practicing his poetry writing. He wanted to learn how to do it better. He knew that writing poetry can be hard sometimes.

Ron's father was helping him write a new poem. Ron was working on a poem for his mother. He wanted to give it to her for her birthday. He decided to write a

poem about when his mom and he played together. Mom was always fun to play with.

Ron's father said that he should try thinking about games that Ron and Mom had played together. Ron remembered that he liked to play hide and seek with his mom. Mom always thought of the best hiding places, and she almost always knew where Ron was hiding, though she didn't say anything right away. She pretended to look for him anyway.

Here is how Ron's poem went:

"Mom, I like to play with you.
You make it fun, whatever we do.
I like to play hide and seek.
You never seem to peek.
Though you know where I hide right away,
You pretend to look for me anyway."

Ron's dad told him that the poem was very good. Ron was proud of it. He hoped that his mom would like the poem for her birthday.

1. What did Ron want to learn to do better?
2. Who helped Ron with his poem?
3. What was Ron's poem about?